It was Sunday.

Mum, Joe and Kate were at home.

They were having dinner.

Mum had finished her dinner.

Joe and Kate had nearly finished

but they had not eaten their carrots.

'Eat the carrots,' said Mum.

'No,' said Joe.

'No,' said Kate.

'Eat the carrots!' said Mum.

'I can not,' said Joe.
'I can not,' said Kate.

'You can eat the carrots,'
said Joe.

'No carrots!' said Joe.